Being Me is a Hot Topic

Written by

Erin Green

Illustrated by Severine Fabienne

Published by Parker & Co., LLC
P.O. Box 50040
Richmond, VA 23250

ISBN: (paperback) 978-1-952733-31-4
ISBN: (hardback) 978-1-952733-32-1
ISBN: (ebook) 978-1-952733-33-8

Dedication

For boys and girls who need help discovering

their uniqueness...YOU, just as you are,

are amazing. You were born to stand out!

For my mom and sister, Desiree,

for always wearing their confidence

and becoming my heroes.

My name is Sasha, and I didn't think

being me would have everyone talking.

I'm free to be me, but I'm not sure

if everyone accepts me as I am.

There are days when others try and bring me down by calling me names. Lucky for me, I have a MOMMA who teaches me everything I need to know about being my best self.

My MOMMA says not to worry about

what others think of me. I am beautiful

just the way I am.

My style is unique, but other kids say I am

funny looking. My MOMMA says,

"Being different is a good thing."

When others say mean things to me,

I still hold my head high.

MOMMA always tells me to say to myself,

" I am beautiful, I am strong, I am unique."

I don't think about the ugly things that people

call me. I am too busy loving me. The way I see it...

I am a work of art, and I have fun choosing what

to wear for school in the morning, even though kids

say mean things about my clothes. Momma says,

"Let them say what they want to say. You're

dressing for yourself. Can't nobody

stop your shine!"

My style lets me express myself. It feels good to be me. MOMMA says I am a ball of sunshine and I shine bright wherever I go!

MOMMA says creativity takes courage, and I am not afraid to be brave! I guess that's why MOMMA is my hero with the superpower of kind words and smiles. She tells me to only allow good thoughts in my head.

MOMMA says that kids are so caught up

in how I look, they don't even notice

it is taking away from loving themselves.

If others cannot accept me for who

I am, I know I can still be great,

because greatness comes from within.

MOMMA tells me I am stronger than I think.

So, I smile from ear to ear!

I am walking into my confidence on my own, and I can now listen to the voice inside my heart. I am ready to show the world who I am.

MOMMA says, "My life is like a fashion show, and the world is my runway."

The sidewalks
are my runways...

The church aisles
are my runways...

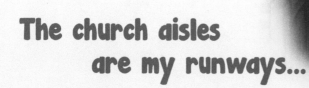

The grocery aisles
are my runways...

The school hallways
are my runways...

Shucks... even when stepping out of

my momma's car, I feel my life is

like my runway.

I am beautifully and wonderfully made.

BEiNG ME iS A HOT TOPiC.

Contestant of VH1's America's Next Top Model: Cycle 24, speaker, mentor, and founder of youth empowerment organization, Twin of A Kind Foundation, Erin Green holds a Master's degree in Marriage Family Therapy. As a victim of bullying, she has defied the odds and realized that the ugliest parts of her story have become the most beautiful parts of her success. With the purpose to empower others to be the best versions of themselves, she has been motivated to turn her own blemishes into success with creating the Model Up program and Pretty Girl Retreat Conference to help young ladies embrace their true potential in order to cultivate and empower their own entrepreneurial spirit. A West Coast native living in Los Angeles, California, she is an identical twin who is separately phenomenal, and together, they are powerful in hosting and runway modeling.

CPSIA information can be obtained
at www.ICGtesting.com
Printed in the USA
BVHW060031060921
615761BV00001B/1